C000087998

OTHER TITLES IN PREPARATION

25 Simple Broadcast Band Aerials
25 Simple Indoor and Window Aerials
25 Simple MW and LW Aerials
25 SWL Technical Activities
25 SWL Listening Activities

25 SIMPLE AMATEUR BAND AERIALS

by
E. M. NOLL

BERNARD BABANI (publishing) LTD
THE GRAMPIANS
SHEPHERDS BUSH ROAD
LONDON W6 7NF
ENGLAND

© 1983 BERNARD BABANI (publishing) LTD

First Published — August 1983

British Library Cataloguing in Publication Data
Noll, Edward M.
   25 simple amateur band aerials. — (BP125)
   1. Antennas (Electronics) — Amateurs' manuals
   I. Title
   621.38'028'3   TK9956

   ISBN 0 85934 100 3

Printed and bound in Great Britain by Cox & Wyman Ltd, Reading

ABOUT THE AUTHOR

Ed Noll is an established American technical author who has written many books, articles and instruction manuals as well as having lectured and taught radio communications at various universities in the U.S.A.

He has worked on the staff of a number of broadcasting stations and as a consulting engineer.

CONTENTS

INTRODUCTION

Many cheap and simple aerials perform very well. Don't let the "keep up with the Jones's aerial-farm phobia" spoil your ham radio enjoyment. You don't need the highest aerials and maximum-gain types to have fun and relaxation. Plan, gather components and erect your own. Be amazed at the fine results you can obtain spending limited funds.

The twenty-five aerials, low cost and sure performers, start with the simple dipole and proceed to beam, triangle and even a mini-rhombic made from four TV masts and about 400 feet of surplus wire.

Economy components were used in constructing all of these aerials over a period of many years. Aerial wire was most often vinyl-covered 16 SWG (14 AWG) or 18 SWG (16 AWG) solid wire that can be found in surplus outlets. Bare stranded 16 SWG or 18 SWG wire was also used. A 20-meter three-element wire beam no more than 16 feet above ground sent out a fine QRP signal across the country.

Masts were largely the TV variety or wooden poles. Popular was the three-section telescoping type, using the bottom two sections without guying for low aerials and one set of nylon guys when stretching up to three section heights. Bases were set down in rocks and sand for a temporary mount; in cement, for more permanent installation. A four-section mast was used for some aerials, but none of the twenty-five aerials were higher than 35 feet (WAC and DXCC were attained with under 200W PEP). Shop for masts at ham and component shops or surplus stores.

The various cables used were RG59U–58U coaxials, 450-ohm open wire, and good quality 300-ohm twin lead. Coaxial line was used for the short aerials; parallel lines for the vee's and rhombics.

A tuner is an excellent investment for the aerial experimenter and multiband operator. Often a limited aerial-point mismatch is not a serious loss problem. The real culprit that such an aerial mismatch causes is the resultant mismatch between line and transmitter that can occur. Modern solid-state transmitter output drops alarmingly with mismatch. A tuner avoids this difficulty. A tuner is essential when using parallel lines. Additional benefits are the reduction in harmonic radiation and, on receive, noise level reduction and less off-channel interference. A big help is an old vacuum-valve design CW transmitter that can be used in tuning aerials and adjusting tuners to near final settings before connection is made to your main transmitter.

After the aerial discussion you will find a complete set of dimension tables that will help you to spot an aerial on a particular frequency. Dimensions are given for various style aerials and other data needed for spacing and cutting phasing lengths. Dimensions for the new WARC bands are also given. Now go on and enjoy yourself!

Be certain to read 1 through 7 before skipping back to other aerial types because many of the ideas introduced can be used in planning and constructing the aerial types that follow.

Ed Noll

1. DIPOLE

The dipole is a half wavelength aerial and is often considered the basic type and a reference aerial when making comparisons with other types. It is usually centre-fed which divides it into two quarter-wavelength segments. End-effect makes the resonant length of a dipole physically shorter than the calculated half-wavelength of free space. In the dimension chart you will notice that free space half-wavelength dimensions are given as well as the required dipole length to obtain resonance at a given frequency. This dimension in the chart considers end-effect.

The dipole aerial has a figure-eight radiation pattern with maximum direction broadside to the wire direction. The lower the aerial is mounted, the less directive and sharp the aerial pattern becomes.

In constructing the aerial it is advantageous to use a dipole-to-coax connector, Fig. 1. The two free ends of the dipole are connected to end insulators. The other end of each insulator is connect to the wire or nylon rope section that attaches to the mast or other support. An attractive alternative is to use nylon rope, running it through a support ring and on down to ground level. Such a halyard provides a convenient means for hoisting or lowering the aerial for making changes or trim-tuning.

Theoretically the dipole should be mounted high and clear and run in a straight true line. Don't you believe it! You can have fun and good results if it is lower, near obstacles, and is even 30 degrees or more departed from a straight-line direction. The ultimate is great! However, sometimes you must think, "Do I need the ultimate to enjoy ham radio?"

More often than not, especially when cutting higher frequency aerials, the aerial is not resonated at the exact frequency you desire. Sometimes the difference is unimportant. However, the influence of aerial's height and nearby obstacles may require additional trimming. An SWR meter is helpful in making such adjustments because the resonant frequency of the aerial system is indicated approximately by the frequency at which there is minimum SWR reading.

3

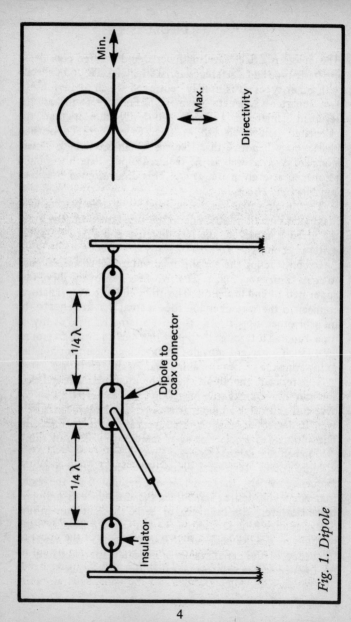

Min.

Max.

Directivity

1/4 λ

1/4 λ

Dipole to coax connector

Insulator

Fig. 1. Dipole

4

2.   HALF-WAVELENGTH SLOPER

The sloper is an economical dipole arrangement that saves ground area and requires but a single high-support structure. The lower support can be a metal or wooden fence post. If the high support is a metal mast, the sloper will have some directivity in the direction of the tilt as shown in Fig.2.

Another advantage is that the aerial can be tuned to a degree at the accessible low end as shown. Sections of wire can be hung on the aerial or a jumper can be used to add a section of line to the aerial length when required. Thus the aerial can be tuned for a minimum SWR at chosen segments of the frequency band. In a typical installation, the top segment of the dipole can be cut to the centre frequency of a given band while the lower segment is cut to a higher frequency. Sections of line can then be jumped or added to this lower segment to move the net resonant frequency about the band for lower SWR when changing operation, for example, between the CW and phone sections of a band.

3.   INVERTED DIPOLE

The popular inverted dipole or inverted-V is shown in Fig.3. This is a fine performing aerial and also requires but a single high-support structure. Popular opinion states that it is more omnidirectional than the straight horizontal dipole. Also there seems to be substantial low angle vertical radiation off the aerial ends, which favors DX operations off the two ends. Often the ends must be shortened to attain resonance on a given frequency because of the influences of ground and apex angle.

An advantage of the inverted dipole that should not be ignored is the ability to tune the aerial at the two accessible ends using hang-on sections of aerial or additional insulators and jumper arrangement as shown previously for the sloper in Fig.2. For example, the quarter-wave segments can be cut at the high-frequency end, say 3.8 MHz on the 80 meter band. By adding equal-length segments to the ends, such an aerial

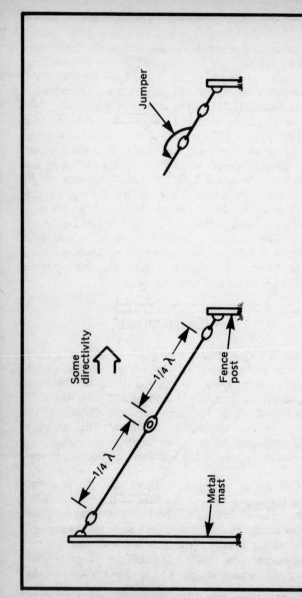

Jumper

Some directivity

1/4 λ   1/4 λ

Fence post

Metal mast

Fig. 2. Sloper

6

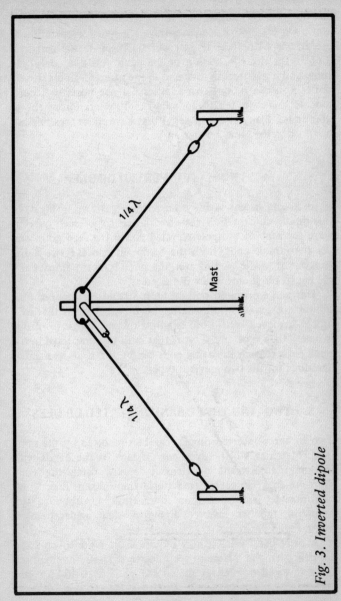

1/4λ

Mast

1/4λ

Fig. 3. Inverted dipole

7

can be made to resonate at a lower frequency position on the band. On 80 metres a quarter-wave segment for operation at 3.8MHz is 61.6 feet. If you wish to resonate the aerial on 3.6MHz in the CW section of the band you need only add three and a half feet to each end of the inverted dipole. If you prefer you can mount two additional fence posts to accommodate this extra length, jumping it into operation whenever you desire. Many styles of aerial that have ends accessible can be tuned in the same manner.

4. TWO-MAST INVERTED DIPOLE

A space and height saving arrangement is shown in Fig.4. In this dipole construction visualize the centre of each quarter-wave segment of a dipole elevated above the feed point and the two dipole ends. Both the feedpoint and the two aerial ends are at low level. However, the aerial is more compact and the height requirements are not as great.

This aerial operated well on both 80 and 160 metres. One should not expect the operation to be the same as that of a dipole stretched out to full length. However, its performance is better than most aerial types that must be compacted into a small space. Again the aerial ends can be tuned in the manner described for the two previous types.

5. TWO- AND THREE-BAND INVERTED DIPOLES

Two or three inverted dipoles can be supported by the same mast. Matching will be excellent on each of the bands with minimum adjustment of element lengths using the same dipole-to-coax connector to a single transmission line. Good performance and minimum interaction is obtained by mounting the two inverted dipoles at right angles to each other, Fig. 5 illustrates.

A three-band version may require a bit more touch-up in adjusting lengths. Maintain a 60 degree separation among the three inverted dipoles, as shown in Fig. 5. A 20-40-80 meter

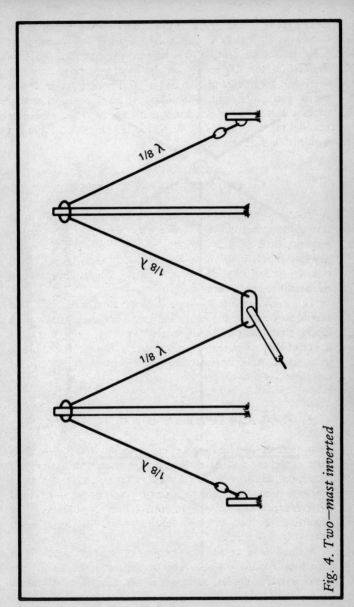

Fig. 4. Two-mast inverted

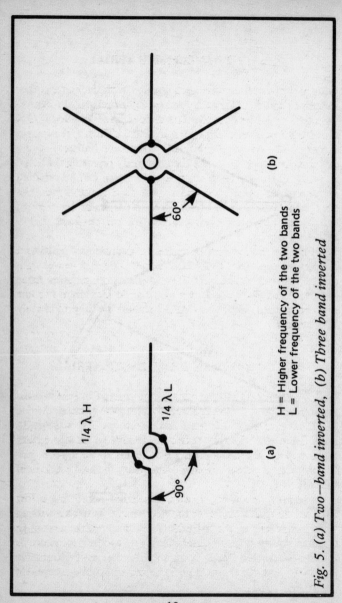

1/4 λ H

1/4 λ L

90°

(a)

60°

(b)

H = Higher frequency of the two bands
L = Lower frequency of the two bands

Fig. 5. (a) Two–band inverted, (b) Three band inverted

10

combination does very well.

6. 3/2 WAVELENGTH AERIAL

Gain in certain directions accompanied with decline in other
directions can be obtained by increasing the length of a centre-
fed aerial to 3/2 wavelength. This divides the aerial into two 3/4
wavelength segments as shown in Fig.6. Thus a reasonable
match can be obtained to a coax transmission line because the
aerial resistance is low at the feed point. By orienting the aerial
properly in its mounting position the pattern can be oriented
in favored directions, particularly the four major lobes. Use
the great circle path angles for your particular location to
orient the aerial mounting position for performance at preferred angles.

A more directional pattern with one pronounced maximum
can be obtained by tilting the legs of the 3/2 wavelength
aerials forward as shown. This construction requires three
support locations but will give you a good maximum in some
specific chosen direction. Angle should be approximately
120 degrees.

7. INVERTED 3/4 WAVELENGTH AERIAL

The 3/2 wavelength aerial can also be erected in inverted-vee
fashion as shown in Fig.7. Dimensions are the calculated value
for 40 metre operation with each segment 3/4 wavelength
long. Some end-trimming may be necessary to set a particular
frequency on the band. This aerial seems to be a good performer with apparent low-angle directivity in the directions of
the wire.

Consider using a tuner with this aerial permitting a low
SWR at the transmitter over the entire band. Tuner advantages
were mentioned in the introduction. An attractive advantage
of tuner use for this particular aerial is its good performance as
a multi-band aerial, from 10 through 80 metres. Performance
on 10, 15 and 40 metres is good, along with quite acceptable

11

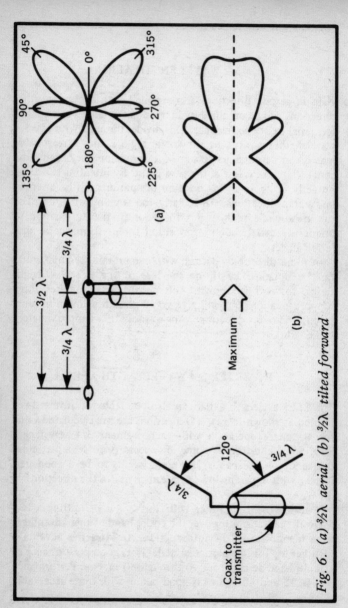

Fig. 6. (a) $^{3}/_{2}\lambda$ aerial (b) $^{3}/_{2}\lambda$ tilted forward

12

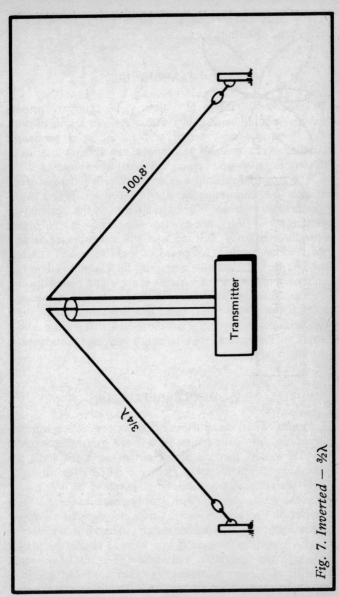

Fig. 7. Inverted — ³⁄₂λ

100.8'

³⁄₄λ

Transmitter

13

results on 20 and 80 metres. An aerial tuner is a necessity for multi-band operation.

8.   RANDOM WIRE

Still another advantage of a tuner is its ability to provide reasonable multi-band results with a random length of wire. This technique may permit you to set up a permanent installation of acceptable performance in a difficult location or to serve as a stop-gap or emergency aerial when required.

The length of random wire serves as both aerial and transmission line, connecting directly to the tuner. It is a single-wire feed arrangement. The overall length of the random wire should be at least one-quarter wavelength at the lowest operating frequency. This can usually be accomplished because the random length is composed of feed-line as well as aerial, see Fig. 8. For 80 metre operation, for example, this would only be some 60 feet. A versatile tuner would permit loading on the higher frequency bands. A disadvantage of this arrangement is the presence of considerable radiation near the tuner and transmitter, especially on those bands where the overall length of the random wire reflects a very high impedance to the tuner output.

9.   DIPOLE—REFLECTOR

A parasitic aerial element has no direct connection with the driven element or the transmission line. A parasitic reflector is cut 5% longer than the driven element and the aerial has maximum directivity away from the reflector as shown in Fig.9. Parasitic elements can be close-spaced or wide-spaced from the driven element. With wide-spacing between 0.2–0.25 wavelength the aerial resistance does not decrease an appreciable amount and a resonable match can be made to a 50-ohm line. A tuner can be used if you wish to obtain the precise match to the transmitter and/or take advantage of the other benefits of a tuner. Close-spacing values are 0.1–0.15 wave-

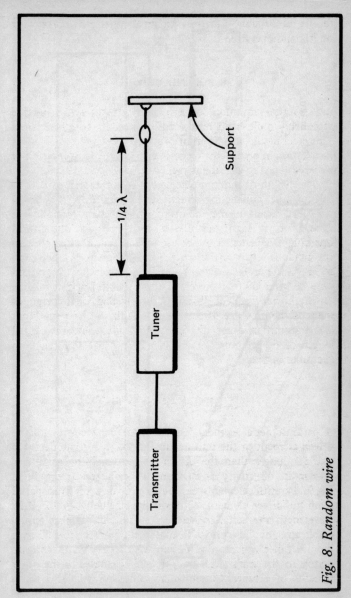

Fig. 8. Random wire

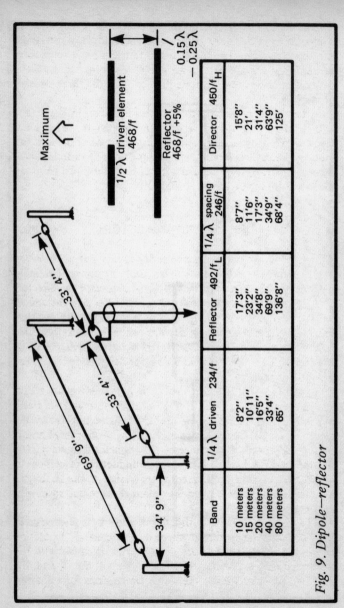

Band	1/4 λ driven 234/f	Reflector 492/f$_L$	1/4 λ spacing 246/f	Director 450/f$_H$
10 meters	8'2"	17'3"	8'7"	15'8"
15 meters	10'11"	23'2"	11'6"	21'
20 meters	16'5"	348"	17'3"	314"
40 meters	33'4'	69'9"	34'9"	63'9"
80 meters	65'	136'8"	68'4"	125'

Maximum

1/2 λ driven element 468/f

Reflector 468/f +5%

0.15 λ
— 0.25 λ

33' 4"

33' 4"

69' 9"

34' 9"

Fig. 9. Dipole—reflector

16

length. In this arrangement the two-element beam is more compact and a bit more gain can be obtained. However, there is a significant decrease in the aerial resistance and some form of matching arrangement is advisable. Matching stubs will be covered in connection with the discussion of the three-element beam.

A two-element beam for 40 metres is shown in Fig.9. The two-elements are spaced a quarter wavelength. Wire aerial elements are suspended between mast pairs. Also included is a table of dimensions for the sideband portions of various bands. Dimensions for other frequencies can be determined from the extensive dimension charts at the end.

10. DIPOLE–DIRECTOR

A director is cut shorter than the driven element as shown in Fig.10. Such a two-element combination shows maximum directivity away from the driven element toward the director. The director is cut 4% shorter than the drive element and, if wide-spaced, there is minimum influence on the dipole aerial resistance. Thus a direct connection can be made to the transmission line. Again a matching arrangement is advisable when close-spacing is used. Typical director lengths for sideband operation are given.

A close-spaced two-element 15 metre beam is shown. A stub-matching plan is shown with both the stub and the transmission line connected to the aerial terminals. In this case the electrical length of the aerial itself has been shortened and it displays a capacitive reactance at the resonant frequency. The shorted stub provides just enough inductive reactance to cancel the capacitive reactance of the aerial. At the same time a resistive impedance match is obtained. Director spacing is only 0.1 wavelength.

The driven element is shortened until it is just slightly longer than the parasitic director. A coaxial T-junction connector is employed at the dipole aerial terminals with the transmission line connected to one side of the T and the shortened coaxial stub to the other. Dimensions for a quarter-

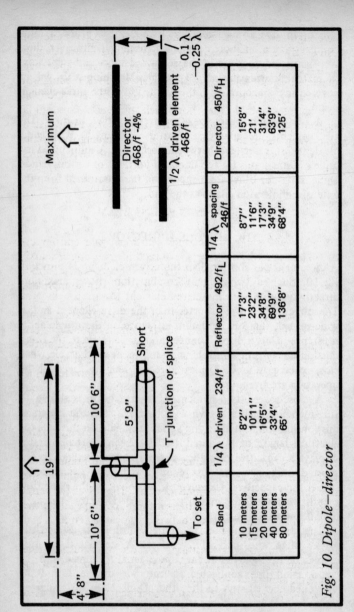

Band	1/4 λ driven 234/f	Reflector 492/f_L	1/4 λ spacing 246/f	Director 450/f_H
10 meters	8'2"	17'3"	8'7"	15'8"
15 meters	10'11"	23'2"	11'6"	21'
20 meters	16'5"	34'8"	17'3"	31'4"
40 meters	33'4"	69'9"	34'9"	63'9"
80 meters	65'	136'8"	68'4"	125'

Director 468/f −4%

1/2 λ driven element 468/f

0.1 λ
−0.25 λ

Maximum

Short

T−junction or splice

To set

5' 9"

10' 6"

10' 6"

19'

4' 8"

Fig. 10. Dipole−director

wavelength section of coaxial line with a velocity factor of 0.66 is given in the dimension charts. A quarter-wavelength section was first used and shorted at the end and then connected to the T junction. Most likely the SWR reading will be high. Now cut off tiny sections of the shorted end of the stub and re-establish the short each time. Do so until a minimum SWR is obtained. In the sample the ideal match came when the stub length was 5'9". A standing wave ratio on the line was 1.05 at 21.3 MHz. Band-end SWR readings were less than 1.15.

11. THREE–ELEMENT BEAM

The three-element beam provides additional gain and directivity. Close-spaced wire beams require less mounting area and, as shown in Fig.11, only four support masts are required. Plastic lines are suspended between the masts to support the driven element.

The two beams shown are dimensioned for operation on 40 and 20 metres. Reflectors are 0.15 wavelength from the driven element; directors, 0.1 wavelength. You will surprised at the results with the beams no more than 16 feet above ground.

Aerial resistance is low and some form of matching is required. Stub matching is suitable and effective when using low-loss parallel lines (450-ohm open line or good quality 300-ohm ribbon line) to connect the beam to the transmitter tuner. The basic stub arrangements are shown in Fig.11. In the first quarter-wavelength section of transmission line beginning at the aerial terminals, the impedance rises from minimum to maximum. Somewhere along this span there is a point of the same impedance as the transmission line. The lower the aerial resistance or the higher the transmission-line impedance, the greater will be the separation between the aerial terminal and the point at which the transmission line is attached for best matching. Try various positions for the transmission line attachment until you locate the point of minimum SWR using your aerial tuner and SWR meter.

The second stub indicates an arrangement that can be used

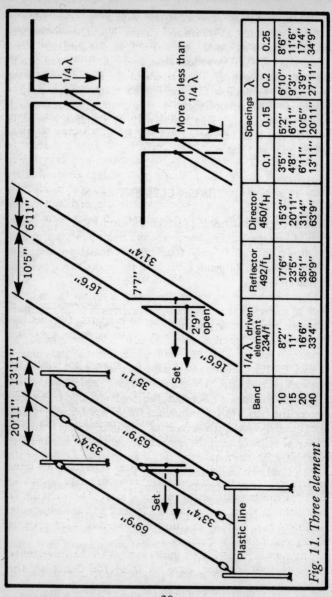

Band	1/4 λ driven element 234/f	Reflector 492/fL	Director 450/fH	Spacings λ			
				0.1	0.15	0.2	0.25
10	8'2"	17'6"	15'3"	3'5"	5'2"	6'10"	8'6"
15	11'	23'5"	20'11"	4'8"	6'11"	9'3"	11'6"
20	16'6"	35'1"	31'4"	6'11"	10'5"	13'9"	17'4"
40	33'4"	69'9"	63'9"	13'11"	20'11"	27'11"	34'9"

Fig. 11. Three element

20

if the aerial also displays a reactive component. A somewhat lower SWR can be squeaked out by making the stub more or less than a quarter wavelength. However, in a practical situation with a quality tuner this step is seldom necessary. If you wish to use the coaxial line the special arrangement of Fig.10 using a foreshortened driven element is convenient and really brings down the SWR on the line.

Matching adjustments with modern solid-state transmitters can be touchy because you must be careful when a high SWR comes on the line in the tuning process. Thus adjustments initially should be made at as low a power level as possible. If you have a particular interest in aerial experimentation, keep an old low-power vacuum-valve transmitter handy. All early trimming and tuning adjustment to the aerial system can be made before the aerial is connected to your main transmitter. Now only touch-up adjustments are needed.

12. PHASED ARRAY

A variety of horizontal phased arrays can be constructed at low cost using wire aerial elements and supports. Two-element end-fire, broadside and collinear styles provide gain and directivity as compared to a single dipole.

The end-fire configuration can be spaced for either bi-directional or uni-directional operation as shown in Fig.12. Two half-wavelength dipoles separated by half wavelength and driven out-of-phase, provide a bi-directional good figure-eight pattern obtaining maximum radiation broadside to the aerial wire if properly fed and tuned. Resultant gain can approach approximately 4dB.

A fine unidirectional cardidoid pattern is obtained by using quarter-wave spacing and quarter-wave feed. As shown in Fig.12, a quarter-wave section of line is located between dipole to which the transmission line is attached and second dipole. Maximum gain is in the direction of dipole that is fed a lagging 90 degrees, shown by the arrow in Fig.12.

The remainder of Fig.12 shows various feed arrangements. In the first set of three, there are three 180 degree end-fire

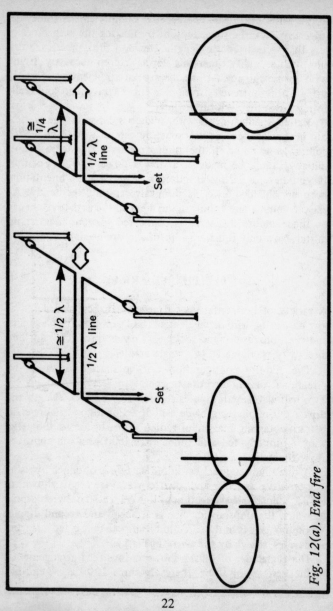

Fig. 12(a). End fire

22

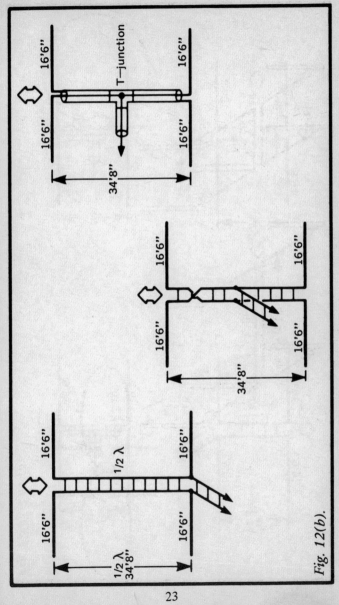

Fig. 12(b).

23

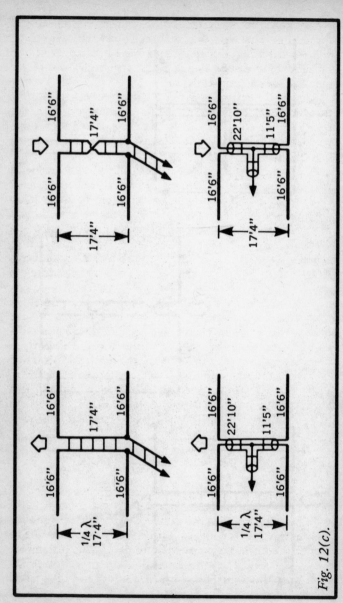

Fig. 12(c).

arrangements. The elongated figure-eight pattern is obtained by feeding one dipole and then the second one 180 degrees later with a half-wave section of line. The same results can be obtained by centre-feeding and then transposing one of the quarter-wave segments as shown.

The third drawing shows the coaxial feed technique. Note that the center conductor of one feed section goes to the left segment of one dipole while the centre conductor of the other goes to the right segment of the second dipole. As a result the two dipoles are fed out-of-phase.

The four remaining drawings demonstrate unidirectional 90 degree feed. Note in the simple parallel feed arrangement that the unidirectional pattern can be shifted by simply transposing the 90 degree feed line that connects between the two dipoles. Unidirectional pattern is always in the direction of the dipole that is fed 90 degrees lagging. When erecting such an aerial you might plan to make it convenient to make such a transposition. It need not be done at the centre as shown but can be accomplished at one of the two dipole feed points.

You can do the same thing using T-junction coaxial feed. In this arrangement there is a half wavelength section of coax from one side of the T-junction to one of the dipoles and a quarter-wave section of feed line to the second. Directivity is determined by proper connection of the inner conductor and shield of the coax segments of the two dipole elements, as shown. Pattern reversal can be obtained simply by transposing either one of the feed lines at the point where it connects to its associated dipole.

13. TWO-ELEMENT BROADSIDE

In a horizontal broadside arrangement the two dipoles are placed one above the other for a two-element combination as shown in Fig.13. Horizontal radiation pattern is a figure-eight with maxima broadside to the plane of the two dipole elements. Both the horizontal and vertical radiation patterns are shown in Fig.13. The vertical radiation pattern is also a figure-eight and, therefore, does some concentrating of the vertical

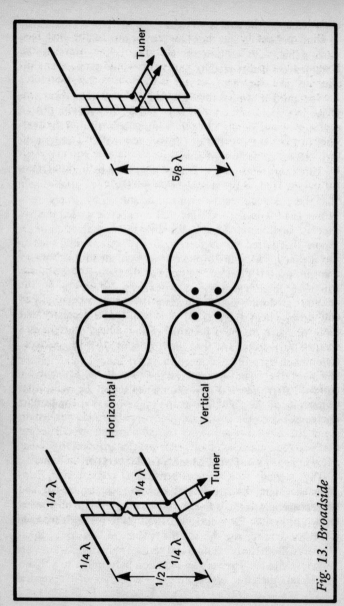

Fig. 13. Broadside

radiation at the favored low angles.

Dipoles must be fed in phase as shown. In the first feed method there is a half-wave section of line between the bottom and top dipoles. Ordinarily this would produce an out-of-phase feed. However, the line is transposed and, therefore, the two dipoles are fed in-phase. Another way of obtaining in-phase feed is to use a centre feed point. Two dipoles can be separated a half wavelength and fed in-phase with this method. Furthermore any separation between the dipoles can be used and in-phase feed will result. If space is available you may wish to try a 5/8 wavelength separation which will result in a further lowering of the vertical radiation angle.

14. COLLINEAR

The horizontal collinear is not used too frequently because of space requirements. However, you may wish to experiment with this phase combination on 10 or 15 metres. In the collinear arrangement, Fig.14, two dipole elements are placed end-to-end. However, for good performance it is necessary that the two ends be well separated. The collinear pattern is a sharpened figure-eight that is broadside to the collinear elements.

Two basic feed arrangements are shown. In the first one the two half-wave elements can be brought near to each other because a high impedance feed is used. Note that the parallel line connects to the two ends of the separate half-wavelength segments. The open-wire line should have an overall length that is an odd-multiple of a quarter-wavelength so as to present a low impedance at the point where it connects to the tuner.

The second feed arrangement is a coaxial line, low-impedance one. Both collinear elements are centre-fed and their respective feed lines are connected to the main coaxial transmission line back to the transmitter by way of a T-junction.

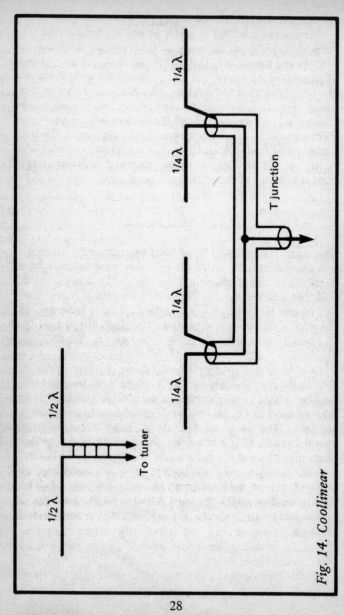

Fig. 14. Coollinear

15. TRIANGLE

The triangle is another low-cost aerial that performs extremely well. It is a full-wavelength aerial, like the quad and delta loop, without being so clumsy and subject to weather damage. It is simple, strong and easy to erect as shown in Fig.15. On 40, 80 and 160 metres, where the other full-wavelength aerials are just about impossible, the triangle is an easy assembly.

The very centre of the full-wavelength wire is attached at the top of the support mast with an insulator. The two legs fan out and fold back on themselves. The ends are returned to the mast to a dipole connector or other form of insulator. The triangle can then be stretched out on each side using nylon rope and two metal fence posts. You will find it is a very rigid assembly, acting also as partial guying for the mast. It is not necessary that the triangle be equal-sided (equilateral). In some mounting situations it may be advantageous to have the triangle base a different length to the other two sides. The important thing is to have the loop resonate as a full wavelength loop.

The base of the triangle need only be 7 to 8 feet above ground to avoid traffic. Aerial impedance is low because the base of the triangle is so near ground. As a result you can make a direct match to coaxial line. The feedpoint at the very centre of the base is accessible using a short stepladder.

A starting point for calculating the length of the triangle wire is the equation for a full wavelength in space (Wire Length = 984 f_{MHz}). The proximity of ground may require that the triangle be shortened somewhat below this calculated value after it is erected. It is easy to do so because of the low height of the wire ends.

When the base of the aerial is raised as it most likely would be for 10, 15, 20 and even 40 metres, the resonant-wire length may even be greater than the full-wavelength free-space calculation. The aerial resistance increases as the triangle is elevated higher above ground and some form of matching may be needed. If you use open-wire line and a tuner this need not be a consideration.

The triangle shows directivity that is broadside to the plane

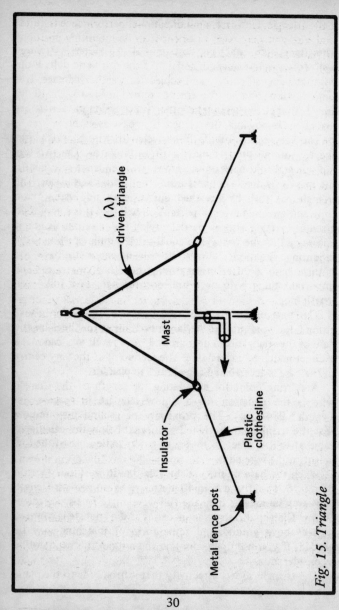

(λ)
driven triangle

Mast

Insulator

Plastic
clothesline

Metal fence post

Fig. 15. Triangle

of the triangle. However, omnidirectional performance is quite good but you may wish to orient it in its mounting position for some favored direction. Orientation can be changed very easily from ground level.

16. HIGH-FREQUENCY TRIANGLE

A high-frequency triangle can be constructed in the two basic ways shown in Fig.16. A wire triangle can be constructed similar to the low-band version. Insulators and nylon rope are attached to the base angles. It can be pulled out and supported from ground level. The wind will not blow this loop down.

An alternative approach is to use self-supporting tubing for the base of the triangle. A thick plastic sheet can be used to support the base elements to the mast. The ends of the tubing can then be linked to the apex of the triangle with wire or additional tubing. Dimensions are given for 20-metre operation. Total length of wire is 69 feet. Stub matching to coax or parallel line can be used. Using parallel line an aerial tuner is all that is necessary. You will be surprised at the performance of this single-element aerial that can be built at such little cost.

17. TWO-ELEMENT TRIANGLE

Reflector and/or director triangles can be added to increase the gain and sensitivity of a triangular configuration in a preferred direction. Spacing between driven triangle and parasitic need only be 0.125 wavelength, Fig.17. This is an 8th wavelength and can be determined by halving the dimension shown under the quarter-wavelength free-space values given in the dimension charts. In general, wire length should be 5% longer for the reflector and 4% shorter for the director. The driven element itself in close proximity to the parasitic element may require additional length. Often the driven element is dimensioned 1000/f instead of the basic 984/f. Reflector would be 5% longer and director 4% shorter than this new value.

31

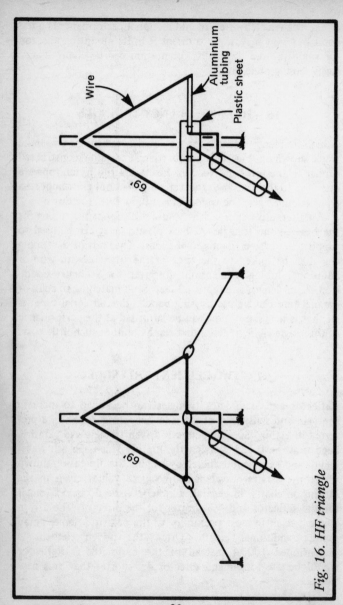

Fig. 16. HF triangle

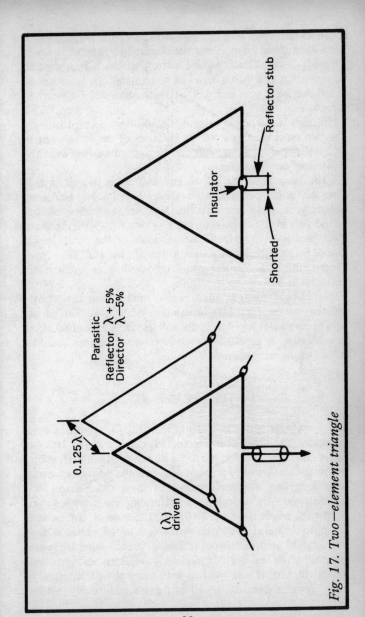

Fig. 17. Two—element triangle

33

In so far as 40, 80 and 160 metre operation is concerned a single additional support mast is required to support the two-element beam. This is indeed a low-cost beam compared to any type of beam that is to be constructed for these bands. Furthermore it is of sound physical structure and not weather-prone.

In high-frequency operation it could be supported strongly by two cross members joining the apex of driven element to apex of parasitic, along with another cross beam between the centres of the two bases.

The lowness of the 40, 80 and 160 metre triangles means the base of the parasitic is accessible. Thus it could be dimensioned to operate as a director. However, an additional stub could be added as shown in Fig.17 along with a sliding short. With the short positioned at the insulator the parasitic will operate as a director. By sliding it down the stub the proper length, the same element could be operated as a reasonable reflector as well.

Additional triangles may be mounted within the triangle of the lowest frequency operation. This is similar to the arrangement employed in multiband quads. A 40 and 80 metre combination is an attractive arrangement. Parasitics could be added in the same manner.

18. LITTLE VEE—BEAM

Did you ever wish to experiment with a vee-beam or a rhombic? You thought it was too expensive and you lack the space. Not so. You can put up a short vee-beam or rhombic. Although performance will not duplicate the performance of a very long one, the performance of these short beams will surprise you. A practical, good performing vee-beam is shown in Fig.18. Leg lengths can be 95—100 feet which corresponds to approximately 3/4 quarter-wavelength on 40 metres. It does fine on 40 metres. Higher-frequency bands have leg wavelengths which exceed 3/4 quarter-wavelength and gain and directivity rise. If you want to send out a good QRP signal in some favored direction on all of these bands the lil'vee-beam

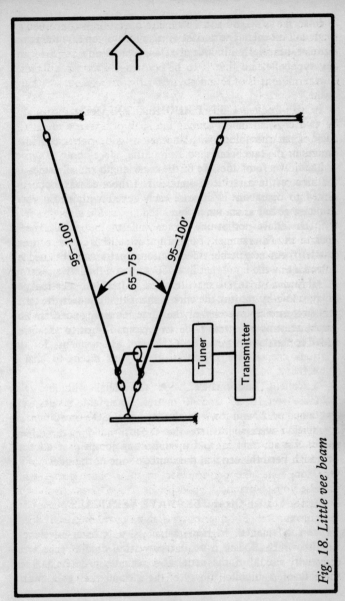

Fig. 18. Little vee beam

deserves a try. Use open-wire line or good-quality 300-ohm line and a tuner. The aerial will also load up on 80 metres and give reasonable results. An apex angle between 65—75 degrees is acceptable.

19. LITTLE RHOMBIC SQUARED

The small rhombic of Fig.19 was our good performer for a number of years. You need a mounting space about 100 foot square. The four sides are of the same length and all angles are 90 degrees. It is a perfect square. The rhombic was supported by four 3-section TV masts, each guyed with nylon rope. Open-wire line and a tuner were used.

The aerial is fed at one corner while the opposite corner is left open. This manner of operation establishes a bi-directional pattern. An acceptable uni-directional pattern is obtained by terminating the far corner in a 450-ohm non-inductive resistor.

If you wish to change the aerial pattern on occasion you may do so by moving the wire jumpers that connect the transmission line to any one of the three remaining corners. You must remember to move the two jumper wires to the other two corners when you do so. Halyard arrangements for the various corners are helpful if it is your intent to change directivity.

Excellent performance with this small rhombic was obtained on 10, 15, and 40 metres. Acceptable results were obtained on 20 and it would also load for QSO's on 80 metres.

If you wish to operate the aerial in an omni-directional fashion you can do so by connecting jumpers at all four corners. Feed the aerial at the centre of one of the sides.

20. QUARTER—WAVE VERTICALS

The fundamental vertical aerial is a quarter-wavelength radiator, Fig.20. This is not a true vertical dipole because the physical length of the aerial approximates just one-half the length of a dipole. However, the ground acts as a mirror

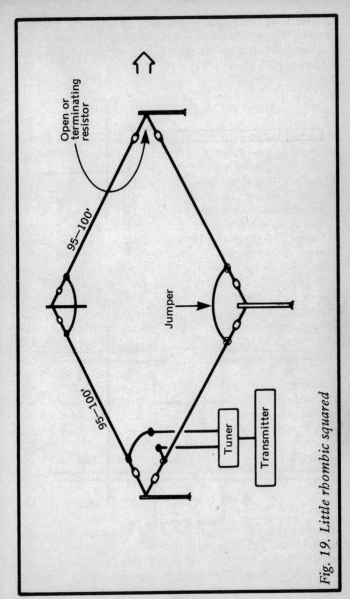

Open or terminating resistor

95—100'

95—100'

Jumper

Tuner

Transmitter

Fig. 19. Little rhombic squared

37

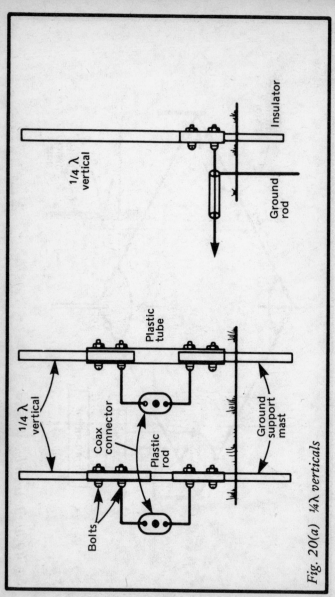

Fig. 20(a) ¼λ verticals

38

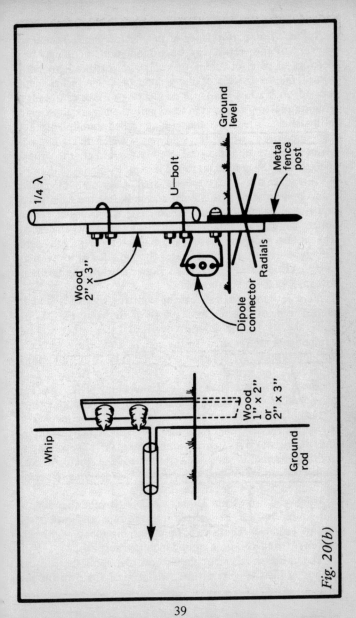

Fig. 20(b)

quarter-wavelength segment. Ground conditions, in fact, have an influence on performance of the vertical aerial. The mirror segment of the vertical can be ground itself, or it may be a network of wires or tubing that acts as an artificial ground. If placed on the surface of the ground or a few inches below ground, such a low-resistance conducting surface can result in a substantial improvement in aerial performance and uniformity of matching. Often a metallic ground (called a ground plane) is also employed when the quarter wavelength radiator is elevated above this physical ground. In effect, the ground plane brings the ground up to the level of the aerial.

An advantage of a vertical aerial is its omni-directional horizontal pattern. It is circular and indicates the radiation of equal level signals in all compass directions. Groups of vertical aerials can be used to obtain a direction pattern when desired. The vertical radiation pattern approximates a half figure-eight. This type of pattern concentrates the radiation at low vertical angles. Little energy is radiated skyward while the favorable low-angle radiation is obtained.

Very low-cost verticals can be constructed for 10 and 15 metres using strong pieces of plastic as shown in Fig.20. The same applies to the 20-metre vertical except that sturdier components are required. In the case of a 40-meter vertical a wooden support system must be constructed to add additional support for the structure.

The first two examples of Fig.20 show how plastic rods and plastic tubes of adequate wall thickness can support a short vertical. The ground rod can be made of the same material as the radiator itself. Holes are drilled through the radiator tubing and the plastic rod. Inserted bolts make the connections to both the radiator and the ground rod. A dipole-to-coax connector can be jumped between the two sections to permit connection of the transmission line.

When you can obtain a thick-wall plastic tube the radiator and ground rod can be inserted into the tube as shown in the second example. These two simple arrangements will easily support 10 and 15 metre ground-mounted verticals.

The third arrangement shows how a long plastic rod can support a light-weight vertical. The vertical fits over the rod and the inner conductor of the coax line connects to one of the holding bolts. A separate ground rod is then connected to the shield of the coax line. No coax connector is needed with this arrangement.

The fourth arrangement shows how a whip vertical can be supported on insulators that are mounted on a wooden 1" x 2" or 2" x 3" batten. Inner conductor connects to the whip and the shield to the ground rod. Ground rod should be 6 to 8 feet long. An alternative is to have a shorter ground rod and then solder or bolt at least four radials to the rod, placing them about one or two inches beneath the ground, stretching them out and separating them by approximately 90 degrees. Resonant-length ¼λ radials help in matching and holding up aerial resistance.

The fifth scheme shows our favorite mounting arrangement. In this arrangement the radiator is U-bolted to a wooden 2" x 3" or 2" x 4" batten. The wooden support is 8 foot long and mounted 3 foot into the ground. A short ground rod is also driven into the ground and has four radials attached to it about an inch and a half below ground level. A dipole-to-coax connector is connected between the bottom U-bolt which supports the radiator and the ground rod. This affords an easy arrangement for connecting the coax line. The radiator can be any size tubing you wish to use for operation on 10, 15 and even 20 metres.

If you wish a very sturdy mount, the ground rod can be a metal fence post.

Furthermore the section of the 2" x 3" or 2" x 4" batten below the vertical radiator can be bolted to the metal fence post. Separation can be such that the dipole connector can be spanned between radiator U-bolt and the bolt that fastens the wooden support to the metal fence post. In our own application the radiator was a two-section TV mast that would permit operation on either 15 or 20 metres because it could be telescoped. This latter method of assembly was helpful in constructing the vertical beams for 15 and 20 metre operation that will be covered later. For 10 and 15 metre operation, two telescoping sections of smaller diameter tubing were used. Shop around at flea markets and surplus outlets, or any place metal tubing is sold, to find a proper combination.

21. TELESCOPING VERTICALS

As mentioned in the previous discussion the ability to
telescope your vertical permits operation on more than one
band. Two 10-foot telescoping sections provide an easy means
of changing over your vertical between 10 and 15 metre
operation, Fig.21. A 5 foot and 7 foot section provide an easy
means for 10 and 15 metre changeover.

To maintain good connections make certain you have a
snug fit and a good low-resistance connection where the inner
tube leaves the outer tube. If you wish you can drill bolt holes
through the two conductors when the two desired resonant
lengths are found.

22. UMBRELLA VERTICALS

Telescoping TV masts function well as vertical quarter-waves
on 40, 80 and 160 metres. A four-section mast can be
extended to the approximate 33 feet needed for 40 metre
operation. The same size mast can also be used on 80 metres
by using aerial wire to extend its resonant length as shown in
Fig.22. The four-section mast can be extended to at least 36
feet. Approximately 24 foot lengths of an aerial wire
connected to the top can produce 80-metre resonance. Three
lengths of aerial wire can be made to extend away from the
top and then supported at ground level using nylon rope. Such
an arrangement performs very well and matches ideally to
50-ohm coaxial line. For best low-angle results use about
9 quarter-wave radials stretched out about 2 inches beneath
the surface. Using a 50-foot telescoping mast fine results were
obtained on 160 metres with umbrella aerial wires about 80
foot long. In all of these umbrella installations it may be necessary to adjust the umbrella wire length to find resonance at a
preferred frequency. However, performance is quite wideband
once you get the resonant length into the band.

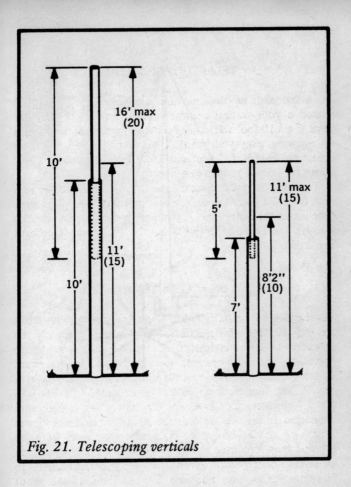

Fig. 21. Telescoping verticals

The base of the vertical was mounted in a wood/cement form and supported by appropriate nylon rope guys. This might be frowned upon as a base insulator. However, it is an economical arrangement and performance was fine. A metallic strap was used to attach the coax connector to the bottom of the vertical while a stiff wire connected the shield side of the coax connector to the radial system.

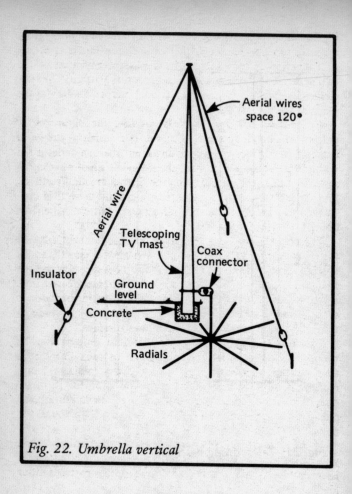

Fig. 22. Umbrella vertical

23. PHASED VERTICALS

The quarter-wavelength verticals described previously can be connected into a variety of directional phased combinations. These combinations produced some surprising DX results despite the fact that they were ground-mounted. Various broadside and end-fire arrangements can be set-up as shown in

Fig.23. In example (i), the two verticals are fed in-phase from a centre junction to which the transmission line is attached. A T-junction is convenient. The in-phase connection of the two verticals set up a figure-eight broadside pattern. The two-element combination is bi-directional perpendicular to the plane of the two aerials.

By feeding the two verticals end-fire, the bi-directional pattern can be along the line of the two aerials as shown in example (ii). In this phasing arrangement the one aerial is fed with the transmission line while the second by a half-wavelength section of line that runs between the first and second verticals. Since your verticals are mounted at ground level it is convenient to change over the directional pattern whenever desired.

Example (iii) shows a 90-degree end-fire connection with the two radiators separated by a quarter-wavelength or 90 degrees. Since the second radiator is fed 90 degrees lagging the first radiator by the 90 degree section of interconnecting line, a cardioid pattern in the direction of the lagging radiator is set-up. This arrangement was described previously in conjunction with the coverage of horizontal phased arrays.

Example (iv) shows how the cardioid pattern can be reversed by using an intervening section of coax line that is three-quarter wavelength long. By so doing, radiator 1 lags radiator 2 by 90 degrees. Dimensions are given for 15 metre operation. Four resonant radials are used. In mounting the radials do not permit the radial for radiator 1 to touch the radial of radiator 2.

In using two element phased verticals, particularly when you plan them to permit change in the directional pattern, it is advisable to use a tuner to insure optimum transmitter loading.

24. TWO-ELEMENT BROADSIDE

Two practical broadside verticals with dimensions for 20 and 40 metre operation are given in Fig.24. In this arrangement centre feed was used to obtain an in-phase feed. It is true that

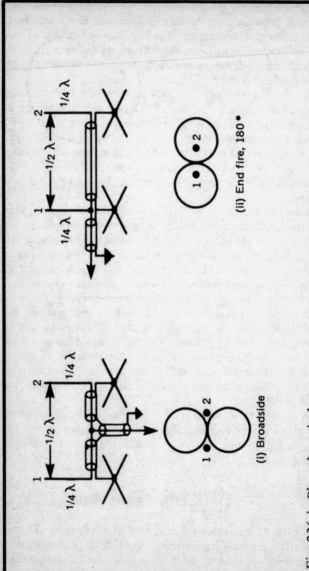

Fig. 23(a) Phased verticals

46

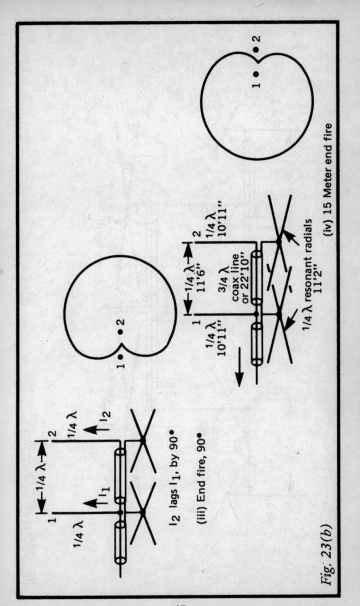

I_2 lags I_1, by 90°

(iii) End fire, 90°

1/4 λ

1/4 λ

I_1

I_2

1/4 λ

1/4 λ 10'11"

1/4 λ 11'6"

3/4 λ coax line or 22'10"

1/4 λ 10'11"

1/4 λ 10'11"

1/4 λ resonant radials 11'2"

(iv) 15 Meter end fire

Fig. 23(b)

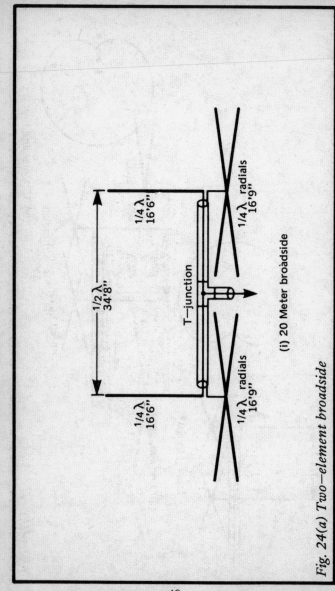

1/2 λ
34'8"

1/4 λ
16'6"

1/4 λ
16'6"

1/4 λ radials
16'9"

1/4 λ radials
16'9"

T—junction

(i) 20 Meter broadside

Fig. 24(a) Two—element broadside

48

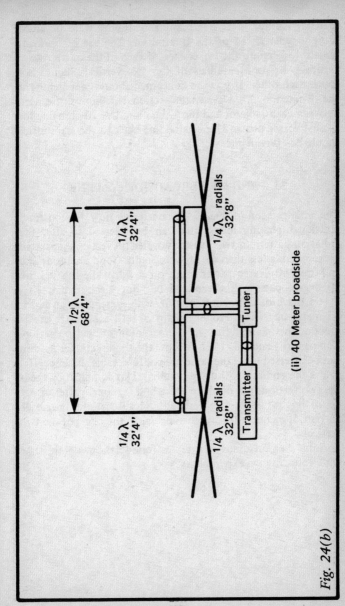

1/2λ
68'4"

1/4λ
32'4"

1/4λ
32'4"

1/4λ radials
32'8"

1/4λ radials
32'8"

Transmitter

Tuner

(ii) 40 Meter broadside

Fig. 24(b)

49

matching is not ideal but reasonable results were obtained using a tuner ahead of the transmitter. The use of resonant radials do keep up the impedance of each of the quarter-wave verticals. Respective radials of the two verticals should not touch each other. If you are concerned about the matching at the T-junction 3/4 wavelength sections of line can be used between each radiator and the T-junction. Use 70-ohm line for these two segments. The coaxial line back to the transmitter should be 50-ohm line.

25. END-FIRE BROADSIDE COMBINE

The arrangement of Fig.25 demonstrates how to construct individual phasing loops that can be inserted to alter the radiation pattern of two quarter-wavelength verticals separated by something less than a half-wavelength. Good broadside and end-fire 180 degree patterns are obtained, while the end-fire 90 degree pattern is acceptable but not ideal. Example (i) shows the broadside configuration with dimensions given for 15 metre operation. Proper lengths of feed cable after the T-junction permit end-fire 90 degree unidirectional operation. Compare (ii) and (iii) to show how the unidirectional pattern can be reversed using the same pre-cut feed cable. Example (iv) shows the end-fire 180 degree cabling. This combination feeds the two verticals out-of-phase and a bi-directional pattern is set up in line with the two verticals. Recall that the broadside pattern of example (i) is perpendicular to the plane of the two verticals.

Some helpful dimension tables follow. Have a good time with your antenna experiments!

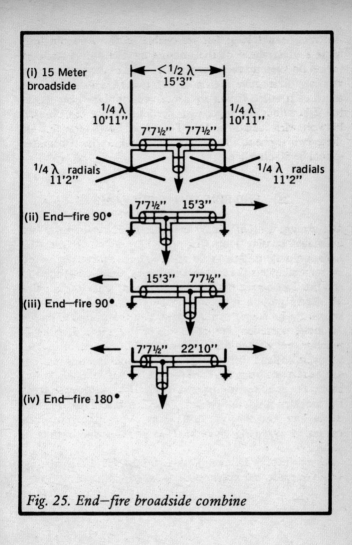

(i) 15 Meter broadside

< ½ λ →
15'3"

¼ λ
10'11"

¼ λ
10'11"

7'7½"   7'7½"

¼ λ radials
11'2"

¼ λ radials
11'2"

(ii) End—fire 90°

7'7½"   15'3"

(iii) End—fire 90°

15'3"   7'7½"

(iv) End—fire 180°

7'7½"   22'10"

Fig. 25. End—fire broadside combine

DIMENSION TABLES

The following tables supply important data useful in the practical dimensioning in feet of aerial systems 2 through 160 metres including the new WARC bands. Dimensions are given for the UK 4 metre band and the USA 6 metre band. A full range of dimensions are given for the 40 and 80 metre bands to accommodate the UK bands as well as the wider USA bands.

Column 1 gives the frequency in MHz. Columns 2 and 3 show the ¼λ and ½λ free space dimensions in feet. This data is helpful in spacing beam elements, both parasitic and phased arrays. Column 4 is the length, in feet, of each quarter-wave side of a dipole. Column 5 is the length, in feet, of a three-quarter side of a 3/2 wavelength aerial. Columns 6 and 7 show the parasitic reflector and director length in feet for beam aerials. Column 8 gives the dimensions, in feet, for the full-wave triangle. Columns 9 and 10 show the length, in feet, of ¼λ and ½λ segments for the common 0.66 velocity factor coaxial line. In using phasing and matching stubs made of coaxial line the velocity factor must be considered.

1 Freq. MHz	2 ¼λ ft.	3 ½λ ft.	4 Dipole ¼λft.	5 ¾λ ft.	6 Refl. ft.	7 Dir. ft.	8 Tri. ft.	9 ¼λ 0.66	10 ½λ 0.66
				160 METRES					
1.81	135.9	271.8	129.3	392.3	271.8	248.6	543.6	89.5	179.0
1.82	135.2	270.3	128.6	390.1	270.3	247.3	540.7	89.0	178.0
1.83	134.4	268.8	127.9	388.0	268.8	245.9	537.2	88.5	177.0
1.84	133.7	267.4	127.1	385.9	267.4	244.6	534.8	88.0	176.1
1.85	133.0	266.0	126.5	383.8	266.0	243.2	531.9	87.6	175.1
1.86	132.3	264.5	125.8	381.8	264.5	241.9	529.0	87.1	174.2
1.87	131.6	263.1	125.1	379.7	263.1	240.1	526.2	86.6	173.3
1.88	130.9	261.7	124.5	377.7	261.7	239.4	523.4	86.2	172.3
1.89	130.2	260.3	123.8	375.7	260.3	238.1	520.1	85.7	171.4
1.90	129.5	258.9	123.2	373.7	258.9	236.8	517.9	85.3	170.5
1.91	128.8	257.6	122.5	371.7	257.6	235.6	515.2	84.9	169.6
1.92	128.1	256.3	121.9	369.8	256.3	234.4	512.5	84.4	168.8
1.93	127.5	254.9	121.2	367.9	254.9	233.2	509.1	83.9	167.9
1.94	126.8	253.6	120.6	366.0	253.6	231.9	507.2	83.5	167.0
1.95	126.2	252.3	120.0	364.1	252.3	230.1	504.6	83.1	166.1
1.96	125.5	251.0	119.4	362.2	251.0	229.6	502.0	82.7	165.3
1.97	124.9	249.7	118.8	360.4	249.7	228.4	499.5	82.2	164.5

| 163.6 | 81.8 | 497.0 | 227.3 | 248.5 | 358.6 | 118.2 | 248.5 | 124.2 | 1.98 |
162.8	81.4	494.5	226.1	247.2	356.8	117.6	247.2	123.6	1.99
					80 METRES				
92.0	46.0	279.5	127.8	139.8	201.7	66.5	139.8	69.9	3.52
91.5	45.8	278.1	127.1	139.0	200.6	66.1	139.0	69.5	3.54
91.0	45.5	276.4	126.4	138.2	199.4	65.7	138.2	69.1	3.56
90.5	45.3	274.8	125.7	137.4	198.3	65.4	137.4	68.7	3.58
90.0	45.0	273.3	125.0	136.7	197.2	65.0	136.7	68.3	3.60
89.5	44.7	271.8	124.3	135.9*	196.1	64.6	135.9	68.0	3.62
89.0	44.5	270.3	123.6	135.2	195.1	64.3	135.2	67.6	3.64
88.5	44.3	269.8	122.9	134.4	194.0	63.9	134.4	67.2	3.66
88.0	44.0	267.4	122.3	133.7	192.9	63.6	133.7	66.8	3.68
87.6	43.8	265.9	121.6	133.0	191.9	63.2	133.0	66.5	3.70
87.1	43.5	264.5	121.0	132.3	190.9	62.9	132.3	66.1	3.72
86.6	43.3	263.1	120.3	131.6	189.8	62.6	131.6	65.8	3.74
86.2	43.1	261.7	119.7	130.9	188.8	62.2	130.9	65.4	3.76
85.7	42.9	260.3	119.0	130.2	187.8	61.9	130.2	65.1	3.78
85.3	42.6	258.9	118.4	129.5	186.8	61.6	129.5	64.7	3.80
84.8	42.4	257.6	117.8	128.8	185.8	61.3	128.8	64.4	3.82
84.4	42.2	256.3	117.2	128.1	184.8	60.9	128.1	64.1	3.84

1 Freq. MHz	2 ¼λ ft.	3 ½λ ft.	4 Dipole ¼λ/ft.	5 ¾λ ft.	6 Refl. ft.	7 Dir. ft.	8 Tri. ft.	9 ¼λ 0.66	10 ½λ 0.66
3.86	63.7	127.5	60.6	183.9	127.5	116.6	254.9	42.0	83.9
3.88	63.4	126.8	60.3	182.9	126.8	116.0	253.6	41.8	83.5
3.90	63.1	126.2	60.0	182.0	126.2	115.4	252.3	41.5	83.1
3.92	62.8	125.5	59.7	181.1	125.5	114.8	251.0	41.3	82.7
3.94	62.4	124.8	59.4	180.2	124.8	114.2	249.7	41.1	82.2
3.96	62.1	124.2	59.1	179.3	124.2	113.6	248.5	40.9	81.8
3.98	61.8	123.6	58.8	178.4	123.6	113.1	247.2	40.7	81.4
40 METRES									
7.02	35.0	70.1	33.4	101.1	70.1	64.1	140.2	23.1	46.2
7.04	34.9	69.9	33.3	100.8	69.9	63.9	139.8	23.0	46.0
7.06	34.8	69.7	33.2	100.6	69.7	63.7	139.4	22.9	45.9
7.08	34.7	69.5	33.1	100.3	69.5	63.5	139.0	22.9	45.8
7.10	34.6	69.3	33.0	100.0	69.3	63.4	138.6	22.8	45.7
7.12	34.5	69.1	32.9	99.7	69.1	63.2	138.2	22.8	45.5
7.14	34.5	68.9	32.8	99.4	68.9	63.0	137.8	22.7	45.4
7.16	34.4	68.7	32.7	99.2	68.7	62.8	137.4	22.6	45.3
7.18	34.3	68.5	32.6	98.9	68.5	62.7	137.0	22.6	45.1

7.20	34.2	68.3	32.5	98.6	68.3	62.5	136.7	22.5	45.0
7.22	34.1	68.1	32.4	98.3	68.1	62.3	136.3	22.4	44.9
7.24	34.0	68.0	32.3	98.1	68.0	62.2	135.9	22.4	44.8
7.26	33.9	67.8	32.2	97.8	67.8	62.0	135.5	22.3	44.6
7.28	33.8	67.6	32.1	97.5	67.6	61.8	135.2	22.3	44.5

20 METRES

14.02	17.5	35.1	16.7	50.6	35.1	32.1	70.2	11.6	23.1
14.04	17.5	35.0	16.7	50.5	35.0	32.1	70.1	11.5	23.1
14.06	17.5	35.0	16.6	50.5	35.0	32.0	70.0	11.5	23.0
14.08	17.5	35.0	16.6	50.4	35.0	32.0	69.9	11.5	23.0
14.10	17.4	34.9	16.6	50.4	34.9	31.9	69.8	11.5	23.0
14.12	17.4	34.8	16.6	50.3	34.8	31.9	69.7	11.5	23.0
14.14	17.4	34.8	16.5	50.2	34.8	31.8	69.6	11.5	22.9
14.16	17.4	34.7	16.5	50.1	34.7	31.8	69.5	11.4	22.9
14.18	17.3	34.7	16.5	50.1	34.7	31.7	69.4	11.4	22.9
14.20	17.3	34.6	16.5	50.0	34.6	31.7	69.3	11.4	22.8
14.22	17.3	34.6	16.5	49.9	34.6	31.6	69.2	11.4	22.8
14.24	17.3	34.5	16.4	49.9	34.5	31.6	69.1	11.4	22.8
14.26	17.3	34.5	16.4	49.8	34.5	31.6	69.0	11.4	22.7
14.28	17.2	34.5	16.4	49.7	34.5	31.5	68.9	11.3	22.7

1 Freq. MHz	2 ¼λ ft.	3 ½λ ft.	4 Dipole ½λ ft.	5 ¾λ ft.	6 Refl. ft.	7 Dir. ft.	8 Tri. ft.	9 ¼λ 0.66	10 ½λ 0.66
14.30	17.2	34.4	16.4	49.7	34.4	31.5	68.8	11.3	22.7
14.32	17.2	34.4	16.3	49.6	34.4	31.4	68.7	11.3	22.6
14.34	17.2	34.3	16.3	49.5	34.3	31.4	68.6	11.3	22.6
15 METRES									
21.02	11.70	23.41	11.13	33.78	23.41	21.41	46.81	7.71	15.41
21.06	11.68	23.36	11.11	33.71	23.36	21.37	46.72	7.69	15.38
21.10	11.66	23.32	11.09	33.65	23.32	21.33	46.64	7.68	15.36
21.14	11.64	23.27	11.07	33.59	23.27	21.29	46.55	7.66	15.33
21.18	11.61	23.23	11.05	33.52	23.23	21.25	46.46	7.65	15.30
21.22	11.59	23.19	11.03	33.46	23.19	21.21	46.37	7.63	15.27
21.26	11.57	23.14	11.01	33.40	23.14	21.17	46.28	7.62	15.24
21.30	11.55	23.10	10.99	33.33	23.10	21.13	46.20	7.61	15.21
21.34	11.53	23.06	10.97	33.27	23.06	21.09	46.11	7.59	15.19
21.38	11.51	23.01	10.95	33.21	23.01	21.05	46.02	7.58	15.15
21.42	11.48	22.97	10.93	33.15	22.97	21.01	45.94	7.57	15.13
10 METRES									
28.2	8.72	17.45	8.30	25.17	17.45	15.95	34.89	5.74	11.49

28.4	8.66	17.32	8.24	25.00	17.32	15.85	34.65	5.70	11.41
28.6	8.60	17.20	8.18	24.83	17.20	15.73	34.41	5.66	11.33
28.8	8.54	17.08	8.13	24.65	17.08	15.63	34.17	5.63	11.25
29.0	8.48	16.97	8.07	24.48	16.97	15.52	33.93	5.59	11.17
29.2	8.42	16.85	8.01	24.32	16.85	15.41	33.70	5.55	11.10
29.4	8.37	16.73	7.96	24.15	16.73	15.31	33.47	5.51	11.02
29.6	8.31	16.62	7.91	23.97	16.62	15.20	33.24	5.47	10.95

6 METRES

50.2	4.90	9.80	4.66	14.14	9.80	8.96	19.60	3.23	6.45
50.6	4.86	9.72	4.62	14.03	9.72	8.89	19.45	3.20	6.40
51.0	4.82	9.65	4.59	13.92	9.65	8.82	19.29	3.18	6.35
51.4	4.79	9.57	4.55	13.81	9.57	8.75	19.14	3.15	6.30
51.8	4.75	9.50	4.52	13.71	9.50	8.69	19.00	3.13	6.25
52.2	4.71	9.43	4.48	13.60	9.43	8.62	18.85	3.10	6.21
52.6	4.68	9.35	4.45	13.50	9.35	8.56	18.71	3.08	6.16
53.0	4.64	9.28	4.42	13.40	9.28	8.49	18.57	3.06	6.11
53.4	4.60	9.21	4.38	13.30	9.21	8.43	18.43	3.03	6.07
53.8	4.57	9.14	4.35	13.30	9.14	8.36	18.29	3.01	6.02

4 METRES

70.1	3.51	7.02	3.34	10.13	7.02	6.42	14.04	2.31	4.62

1	2	3	4	5	6	7	8	9	10
Freq. MHz	¼λ ft.	½λ ft.	Dipole ½λ ft.	¾λ ft.	Refl. ft.	Dir. ft.	Tri. ft.	¼λ 0.66	½λ 0.66
70.3	3.50	7.00	3.33	10.10	7.00	6.40	14.00	2.30	4.61
70.6	3.49	6.97	3.32	10.06	6.97	6.37	13.94	2.29	4.59

2 METRES

1	2	3	4	5	6	7	8	9	10
144.4	1.70	3.41	1.62	4.92	3.41	3.12	6.81	1.12	2.24
144.8	1.70	3.40	1.62	4.90	3.40	3.11	6.80	1.12	2.23
145.2	1.69	3.39	1.61	4.89	3.39	3.10	6.78	1.12	2.23
145.6	1.69	3.38	1.61	4.88	3.38	3.09	6.76	1.11	2.23
146.0	1.68	3.37	1.60	4.86	3.37	3.08	6.74	1.11	2.22
146.4	1.68	3.36	1.60	4.85	3.36	3.07	6.72	1.11	2.21
146.8	1.68	3.35	1.59	4.84	3.35	3.07	6.70	1.11	2.21
147.2	1.67	3.34	1.59	4.82	3.34	3.06	6.68	1.10	2.20
147.6	1.67	3.33	1.59	4.81	3.33	3.05	6.67	1.10	2.20

NEW WARC BANDS

30 METRES

1	2	3	4	5	6	7	8	9	10
10.02	24.6	49.1	23.35	70.9	49.1	44.9	98.2	16.17	32.33
10.04	24.5	49.0	23.31	70.7	49.0	44.8	98.0	16.14	32.27

10.06	24.5	48.9	23.26	70.6	48.9	44.7	97.8	16.10	32.20
10.08	24.4	48.8	23.21	70.4	48.8	44.6	97.6	16.07	32.14
10.10	24.4	48.7	23.17	70.3	48.7	44.6	97.4	16.04	32.08
10.12	24.3	48.6	23.12	70.2	48.6	44.5	97.2	16.01	32.02
10.14	24.3	48.5	23.08	70.0	48.5	44.4	97.0	15.98	31.95

17 METRES

18.08	13.61	27.21	12.94	39.30	27.21	24.89	54.42	8.96	17.92
18.10	13.59	27.18	12.93	39.23	27.18	24.86	54.36	8.95	17.90
18.12	13.58	27.15	12.92	39.22	27.15	24.83	54.30	8.94	17.88
18.14	13.56	27.12	12.91	39.21	27.12	24.81	54.24	8.93	17.86
18.16	13.55	27.09	12.90	39.21	27.09	24.78	54.18	8.92	17.84

12 METRES

24.92	9.87	19.74	9.39	28.5	19.74	18.06	39.49	6.50	13.00
24.94	9.86	19.73	9.38	28.5	19.73	18.04	39.45	6.50	12.99
24.96	9.86	19.72	9.37	28.4	19.72	18.03	39.42	6.49	12.98
24.98	9.85	19.71	9.36	28.4	19.71	18.01	39.39	6.49	12.97

LENGTH CONVERSION TABLE

The table below is an aid in converting feet in decimals to decimal inches and then to practical tape-lengths. For example, an element that is 31.5 feet is 31 feet 6 inches. An aerial which is 12.35 feet is approximately 12′ 4¼″. These are not exact values but are practical in terms of cutting a length with a tape measure. Inches equals decimal part of a foot times 12.

Decimal ft.	Decimal in.	Tape in.
.05	0.6	⅝
.10	1.2	1¼
.15	1.8	1⅞
.20	2.4	2⅜
.25	3.0	3
.30	3.6	3⅝
.35	4.2	4¼
.40	4.8	4⅞
.45	5.4	5⅜
.50	6.0	6
.55	6.6	6⅝
.60	7.2	7¼
.65	7.8	7⅞
.70	8.4	8⅜
.75	9.0	9
.80	9.6	9⅝
.85	10.2	10¼
.90	10.8	10⅞
.95	11.4	11⅜

EQUATIONS

¼λ Free Space	=	$246/f_{MHz}$
½λ Free Space	=	$492/f_{MHz}$
¼λ Dipole	=	$234/f_{MHz}$
¾λ Dipole	=	$710/f_{MHz}$
Reflector	=	$492/f_{MHz}$
Director	=	$450/f_{MHz}$
Triangle	=	$984/f_{MHz}$
¼λ x 0.66VF	=	$162/f_{MHz}$
½λ x 0.66VF	=	$324/f_{MHz}$

TYPES OF CABLES

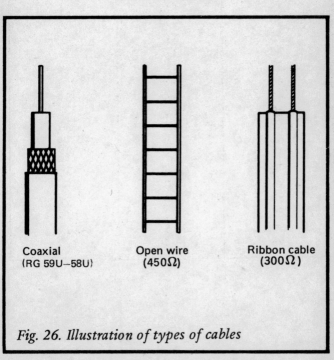

Coaxial
(RG 59U—58U)

Open wire
(450Ω)

Ribbon cable
(300Ω)

Fig. 26. Illustration of types of cables

ALSO OF INTEREST

BP105: AERIAL PROJECTS
R. A. Penfold

Whether you have built a very simple short wave receiver or have purchased a most sophisticated piece of equipment, the performance you achieve will ultimately depend on the aerial to which your set is connected.

The subject of aerials is vast but in this book the author has considered practical aerial designs, including active, loop and ferrite aerials which give good performances and are relatively simple and inexpensive to build. The complex theory and mathematics of aerial design have been avoided.

Also included are constructional details of a number of aerial accessories including a preselector, attenuator, filters and tuning unit.

96 pages *1982*
0 85934 080 5 **£1.95**

BP91: AN INTRODUCTION TO RADIO DXING
R. A. Penfold

There is a strange fascination in being able to listen in your own living room to a broadcast, be it commercial or by a radio amateur, which is being transmitted from a location many thousands of miles away, possibly across the other side of the world.

Anyone can switch on a short wave receiver and play with the controls until they pick up something, but to find a particular station, country or type of broadcast and to receive it as clearly as possible with the minimum of distortion and interference requires a little more skill and knowledge. The object of this book is to help the reader do just that, which in essence is the fascination hobby of radio DXing.

The book is divided into two main sections, one devoted to amateur band reception and the other covering broadcast band reception, with advice on suitable equipment and the techniques employed when using the equipment. Also, for those interested in actually building projects, the construction of a number of useful accessories are described.

112 pages *1981*
0 85934 066 X **£1.95**

Notes

Notes

Notes

Please note overleaf is a list of other titles that are available in our range of Radio, Electronics and Computer Books.

These should be available from all good Booksellers, Radio Component Dealers and Mail Order Companies.

However, should you experience difficulty in obtaining any title in your area, then please write directly to the publisher enclosing payment to cover the cost of the book plus adequate postage.

If you would like a complete catalogue of our entire range of Radio, Electronics and Computer Books then please send a Stamped Addressed Envelope to:

BERNARD BABANI (publishing) LTD
THE GRAMPIANS
SHEPHERDS BUSH ROAD
LONDON W6 7NF
ENGLAND